Grades 7–8   Violin

Improve your sight-reading!

Paul Harris

FABER *ff* MUSIC

Here is some guidance as to what should be in your mind as you prepare to give a musical performance when sight-reading:

- **Choose a suitable tempo** A lighter approach can help in giving the impression of speed whereas a more sustained quality of sound is appropriate in slower music.
- **Keep the pulse even and steady** If you follow the instructions in this book to count two bars in you'll have no trouble establishing a steady pulse. This will also help any musical *rubato* (appropriate in many styles of music) to sound more convincing.
- **Give energy to the rhythm** Use occasional (and usually unmarked) accentuation to help drive the music forward.
- **Shape the phrases** Gentle (unmarked) crescendos when ascending and diminuendos when descending often help to shape phrases. Try to think where each phrase is leading to.
- **Follow dynamics and other markings** These are very important in helping to bring music to life. Add more of your own if you feel they would enhance the character or add more personality to the performance.
- **Think in the key** In your sight-reading practice, always play the scale and arpeggio (preferably from notation) as part of your preparation.
- **Give musical character to your performance** Just like an actor gets 'in character' before a performance, think about what you want to convey and keep this strongly in mind as you play. Develop your ability to understand what a piece is saying before you begin playing.

With many thanks to Gillian Secret for her invaluable help.

© 2011 by Faber Music Ltd
This edition first published in 2011 by Faber Music Ltd.
Bloomsbury House 74–77 Great Russell Street London WC1B 3DA
Music processed by Donald Thomson
Cover and page design by Susan Clarke
Cover illustration by Drew Hillier
Printed in England by Caligraving Ltd
All rights reserved

ISBN10: 0-571-53627-1
EAN13: 978-0-571-53627-6

US edition:
ISBN10: 0-571-53667-0
EAN13: 978-0-571-53667-2

To buy Faber Music publications or to find out about the full range of titles available please contact your local music retailer or Faber Music sales enquiries:
Faber Music Ltd, Burnt Mill, Elizabeth Way, Harlow CM20 2HX
Tel: +44 (0) 1279 82 89 82   Fax: +44 (0) 1279 82 89 83
sales@fabermusic.com   fabermusicstore.com

Introduction

Being a good sight-reader is so important and it's not difficult at all! If you work through this book carefully – always making sure that you really understand each exercise before you play it, you'll never have problems learning new pieces or doing well at sight-reading in exams!

Using the workbook

1 Rhythmic exercises
Make sure you have grasped these fully before you go on to the melodic exercises: it is vital that you really know how the rhythms work. There are a number of ways to do the exercises – see *Improve your sight-reading* Grade 1 for more details, or these ideas can be downloaded from *fabermusicstore.com* (under the publication title).

2 Melodic exercises
These exercises use just the notes (and rhythms) for the Stage, and are organised into Sets which progress gradually. If you want to sight-read fluently and accurately, get into the simple habit of working through each exercise in the following ways before you begin to play it:
- Make sure you understand the rhythm and counting. Clap the exercise through.
- Know what notes you are going to play and the fingering you are going to use.
- Try to hear the piece through in your head. Always play the first note to help.
- Try to experiment with a variety of fingerings in your sight-reading. In some pieces, choosing a more ambitious fingering (which might involve 2nd or 4th position) could produce a better musical result.

3 Prepared pieces
Work your way through the questions first, as these will help you to think about or 'prepare' the piece. Don't begin playing until you are pretty sure you know exactly how the piece goes.

4 Going solo!
It is now up to you to discover the clues in this series of practice pieces. Give yourself about a minute and do your best to understand the piece before you play. Check the rhythms and fingering, hear the piece in your head and then play it confidently.

Always remember to feel the pulse and to keep going steadily once you've begun. Good luck and happy sight-reading!

Terminology:
Bar = measure

Grade 7 **Stage 1**

Rhythmic exercises

Always count at least two bars before you begin each exercise –
one out loud and one silently.

Melodic exercises

Set 1: Exploring F♯ minor

Set 2: Extending the range to top G

There are many ways to finger these pieces: the fingerings here are suggestions. You may prefer to use 2nd and 4th positions.

Prepared piece

1 Play the scale and arpeggio in a variety of dynamics found in this piece.

2 Hear the rhythmic pattern of the first two bars in your head. Now improvise a short piece on the rhythm.

3 Think through how you will finger the piece. Then think through the bowing.

4 Tap the pulse and think the rhythm, then tap the rhythm and think the pulse.

5 Make up an exercise based on bar 15.

6 Read the piece through silently (having played the first note), thinking about expressing the character as you do so.

Hot air ballooning on a calm day (with sandwiches)

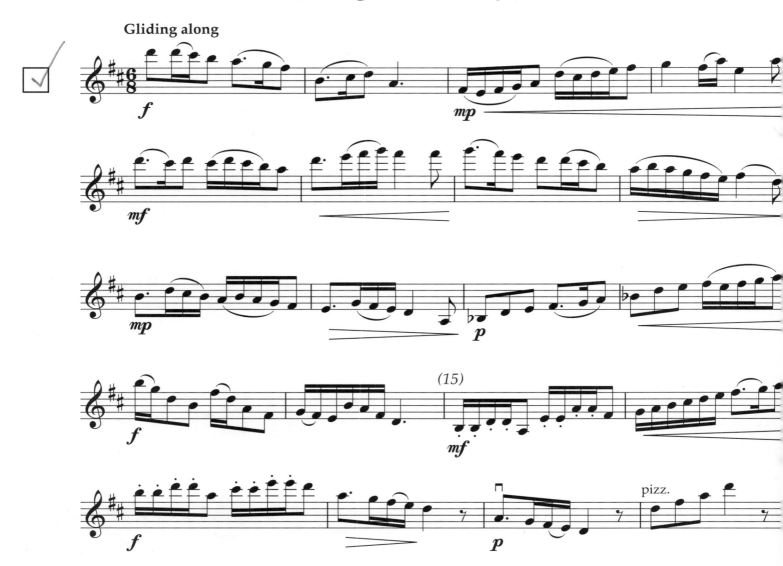

Going solo! Don't forget to prepare each piece carefully before you play it.

Checkmate

Dancing on the banks of the Berezayka

Very high five!

Grade 7 Stage 2

Rhythmic exercises

Feel the beat strongly in these exercises, especially when
ties are involved.

Melodic exercises

Set 1: Exploring more ties

Set 2: Exploring more flat keys

Prepared piece

1 Play the 3 octave scale and arpeggio in the character of the piece.

2 Improvise a short piece in the key, using the rhythm of the first two bars.

3 Think through the piece in terms of bow speed.

4 Think about fingering and where to shift.

5 Play the first note and hear the piece through in your head, with musical expression.

6 Now play it as if you really know the piece – with great confidence!

Andalusian night music for a lone Spanish guitarist

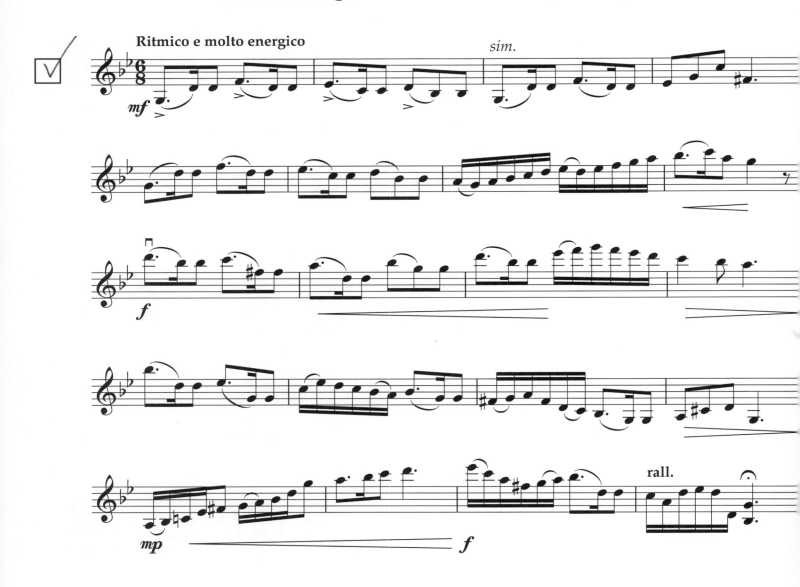

Going solo! Don't forget to prepare each piece carefully before you play it.

Five go on an adventure

On a dark and stormy night ...

Grade 7 **Stage 3**

Irregular time signature $\frac{7}{8}$ and $\frac{7}{4}$
Left-hand pizzicato

Rhythmic exercises

Melodic exercises

Set 1: Exploring $\frac{7}{8}$ time

Look out for 3+4 and 4+3 groupings in $\frac{7}{8}$

Set 2: Exploring 7/4

Set 3: Both time signatures

Prepared piece

1 Play the scale and arpeggio in the character of the piece.

2 Look at the first bar plus the next three notes for about 10 seconds, then play them from memory.

3 How many times does that pattern return?

4 Now improvise a short piece in this key, using that pattern.

5 Read the piece through in your head, in time, thinking about the fingering and shifting.

6 Feel the quaver pulse for a couple of bars, then set off confidently and play without any hesitations.

Dance of the annoying hiccups

Going solo! Don't forget to prepare each piece carefully before you play it.

Dancing the night away

Black, no sugar

Grade 7 Stage 4

Brandenburg concerto no.7

What shall we do with the very drunk sailor?

Paul Harris's Exam Workout!

IMPROVE YOUR SIGHT-READING!

The ability to sight-read fluently is an important part of musical training, whether intending to play professionally, or simply for enjoyment. By becoming a good sight-reader, the player will be able to learn pieces more quickly, play duets and chamber music with confidence and assurance. Also, in grade examinations, a good performance in the sight-reading test will result in useful extra marks!

Improve your sight-reading! is a series of workbooks designed to help incorporate sight-reading regularly into practice and lessons, and to help prepare for the sight-reading test in grade examinations. It offers a progressive series of enjoyable and stimulating stages which, with careful work, should result in considerable improvement from week to week.

Step by step, the player is encouraged to build up a complete picture of each piece. Rhythmic exercises help develop and maintain a steady beat, whilst melodic exercises assist in the recognition of melodic shapes at a glance. The study of a prepared piece with associated questions for the student to answer helps consolidate acquired skills and, finally, the real, unprepared sight-reading test itself.

Such practical and methodical material is guaranteed to take the horror out of sight-reading!

0-571-53621-2	Violin Grade 1	NEW EDITION
0-571-53622-0	Violin Grade 2	NEW EDITION
0-571-53623-9	Violin Grade 3	NEW EDITION
0-571-53624-7	Violin Grade 4	NEW EDITION
0-571-53625-5	Violin Grade 5	NEW EDITION
0-571-53626-3	Violin Grade 6	NEW EDITION
0-571-53627-1	Violin Grades 7–8	NEW EDITION
0-571-51075-2	Viola Grades 1–5	
0-571-51873-7	Cello Grades 1–3	
0-571-51874-5	Cello Grades 4–5	
0-571-51149-X	Double Bass Grades 1–5	
0-571-51373-5	Descant Recorder Grades 1–3	
0-571-51466-9	Flute Grades 1–3	
0-571-51467-7	Flute Grades 4–5	
0-571-51789-7	Flute Grade 6	
0-571-51790-0	Flute Grades 7–8	
0-571-51464-2	Clarinet Grades 1–3	
0-571-51465-0	Clarinet Grades 4–5	
0-571-51787-0	Clarinet Grade 6	
0-571-51788-9	Clarinet Grades 7–8	

0-571-51635-1	Saxophone Grades 1–3
0-571-51636-X	Saxophone Grades 4–5
0-571-51633-5	Oboe Grades 1–3
0-571-57021-6	Oboe Grades 4–5
0-571-51148-1	Bassoon Grades 1–5
0-571-51076-0	Horn Grades 1–5
0-571-50989-4	Trumpet Grades 1–5
0-571-51152-X	Trumpet Grades 5–8
0-571-56860-2	Trombone Grades 1–5
0-571-53300-0	Piano Pre-Grade 1
0-571-53301-9	Piano Grade 1
0-571-53302-7	Piano Grade 2
0-571-53303-5	Piano Grade 3
0-571-53304-3	Piano Grade 4
0-571-53305-1	Piano Grade 5
0-571-53306-X	Piano Grade 6
0-571-53307-8	Piano Grade 7
0-571-53308-6	Piano Grade 8

IMPROVE YOUR AURAL!

The very thought of aural, especially in examinations, strikes fear into the heart of many young pianists and instrumentalists. But aural should not be an occasional optional extra – it's something to be developing all the time, because having a good ear will help improve musicianship more than any other single musical skill.

Improve your aural! is designed to take the fear out of aural. Through fun listening activities, boxes to fill in and practice exercises, these workbooks and CDs focus on all the elements of the ABRSM aural tests. Because all aspects of musical training are of course connected, the student will also be singing, clapping, playing their instrument, writing music down, improvising and composing – as well as developing that vital ability to do well at the aural test in your grade exams!

0-571-53438-4	Grade 1 (with CD)	NEW EDITION
0-571-53439-2	Grade 2 (with CD)	NEW EDITION
0-571-53544-5	Grade 3 (with CD)	NEW EDITION
0-571-53545-3	Grade 4 (with CD)	NEW EDITION
0-571-53546-1	Grade 5 (with CD)	NEW EDITION
0-571-53440-6	Grade 6 (with CD)	NEW EDITION
0-571-53441-4	Grades 7–8 (with CD)	NEW EDITION

IMPROVE YOUR PRACTICE!

Improve your practice! is the essential companion for pianists or instrumentalists, encapsulating Paul Harris's failsafe approach to learning.

With boxes for filling in, make-your-own playing cards, a handy practice diary and, when needed, an exam countdown, these books help to explore the pieces and to understand their character. The books will enable the student to develop ways of getting the most out of their practice sessions – whatever their length.

Most importantly, the wider musical skills such as aural, theory, sight-reading, improvisation and composition develop alongside, resulting in a more intelligent and all-round musician. Practice makes perfect!

0-571-52271-8	Instrumental Grade 1
0-571-52272-6	Instrumental Grade 2
0-571-52273-4	Instrumental Grade 3
0-571-52274-2	Instrumental Grade 4
0-571-52275-0	Instrumental Grade 5
0-571-52844-9	Piano Beginners
0-571-52261-0	Piano Grade 1
0-571-52262-9	Piano Grade 2
0-571-52263-7	Piano Grade 3
0-571-52264-5	Piano Grade 4
0-571-52265-3	Piano Grade 5

IMPROVE YOUR TEACHING!

Energising and inspirational, **Improve your teaching!** and **Teaching Beginners** are 'must have' handbooks for all instrumental and singing teachers. Packed full of comprehensive advice and practical strategies, they offer creative yet accessible solutions to the challenges faced in music education.

Group Music Teaching in Practice is a major new resource designed to help class teachers, instrumental teachers and music services collaborate and refine their skills to enable them to deliver an holistic primary music curriculum. This book will help all teachers involved in group teaching programmes

These insightful volumes are distilled from years of personal experience and research. In his approachable style, Paul Harris outlines his innovative strategy of 'simultaneous learning' as well as offering advice on lesson preparation, aural and memory work, effective practice and more.

0-571-52534-2	Improve your teaching!
0-571-53175-X	Improve your teaching! Teaching beginners
0-571-53319-1	Group Music Teaching in Practice (with ECD)

IMPROVE YOUR SCALES!

Paul Harris's **Improve your scales!** is the only way to learn scales.

The purpose of the workbooks is to incorporate regular scale playing into lessons and daily practice, and to help pupils prepare for grade examinations. Each volume contains all the scales, arpeggios and ranges required for the relevant Associated Board exam, along with complementary practical material. 'Know your notes!' makes sure the actual notes *are* known!; 'finger fitness' exercises cover technically tricky areas and the scales, arpeggios and broken chord study pieces place the material in a more musical context. Simple improvisations and even an opportunity to 'have a go' at composing a short tune encourage thought 'in the key'.

This unique approach encourages the student to understand and play comfortably within in a key, thus helping them pick up those valuable extra marks in exams, as well as promoting a solid basis for the learning of repertoire and for sight-reading.

0-571-51663-7	Violin Grades 1–2
0-571-51664-5	Violin Grade 3
0-571-51665-3	Violin Grade 4
0-571-51666-1	Violin Grade 5
0-571-52024-3	Flute Grades 1–3
0-571-52025-1	Flute Grades 4–5
0-571-51475-8	Clarinet Grades 1–3
0-571-51476-6	Clarinet Grades 4–5
0-571-53411-2	Piano Grade 1
0-571-53412-0	Piano Grade 2
0-571-53413-9	Piano Grade 3
0-571-53414-7	Piano Grade 4
0-571-53415-5	Piano Grade 5

Faber Music Limited
Burnt Mill, Elizabeth Way, Harlow, Essex CM20 2HX. Tel: +44 (0)1279 828982 Fax: +44 (0)1279 828
www.fabermusicstore.com

From major to minor

Merry morris dancing in May

Grade 8 **Stage 1**

Rhythmic exercises

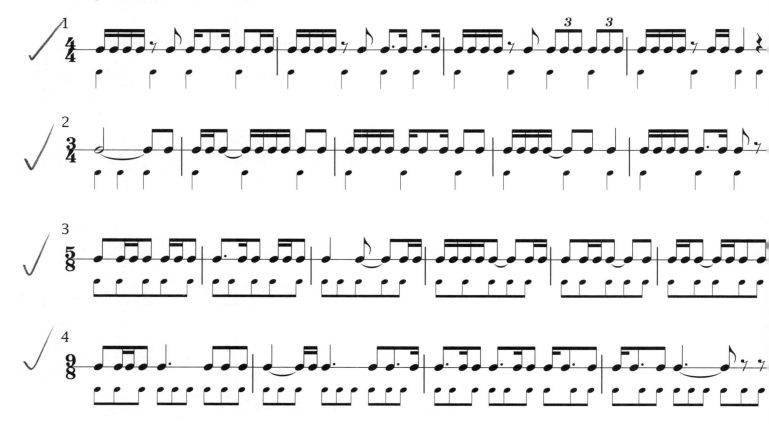

Melodic exercises

Set 1 : Exploring B major

Set 2: Extending the range to top A

Prepared piece

> **1** Play the scale and arpeggio in an agitated character.
>
> **2** Have a look at bar 6 for about 5 seconds then play it from memory. Now improvise a piece based on that rhythm, in the same key.
>
> **3** Think through how you will finger the piece. Now think through the bowing.
>
> **4** Tap the rhythm with your left hand for bar 1, right hand for bar 2, left hand for bar 3, and so on.
>
> **5** Read through the piece confidently in your head.
>
> **6** Play the piece confidently, ignoring any slight mishaps that may occur.

Oh no, I'm late!

Going solo! Don't forget to prepare each piece carefully before you play it.

Grand march from Cremona

The lark descending

Grade 8 **Stage 2**

Rhythmic exercises

Melodic exercises

Set 1: Exploring D♭ major and F minor

Set 2: Exploring trills, grace notes and mordents

Prepared piece

1 Improvise in the key using lots of scale and arpeggio patterns and mordents.

2 Can you find where the opening music returns? How is it different?

3 Think about the bowing and bow speed.

4 Tap the rhythm with one hand and a quaver pulse with the other.

5 Play the first note and (tapping the pulse) read through the piece, hearing it in your head as accurately as you can. If you're not sure of an interval just make your best guess.

6 Study the first few notes (up to the A♭ in bar 2) for about 10 seconds then play the passage from memory.

Sad song and slow dance

Going solo! Don't forget to prepare each piece carefully before you play it.

Song for a lonely seafarer

The sky was bleak, the wind whistled, a strange wailing in the distance ...

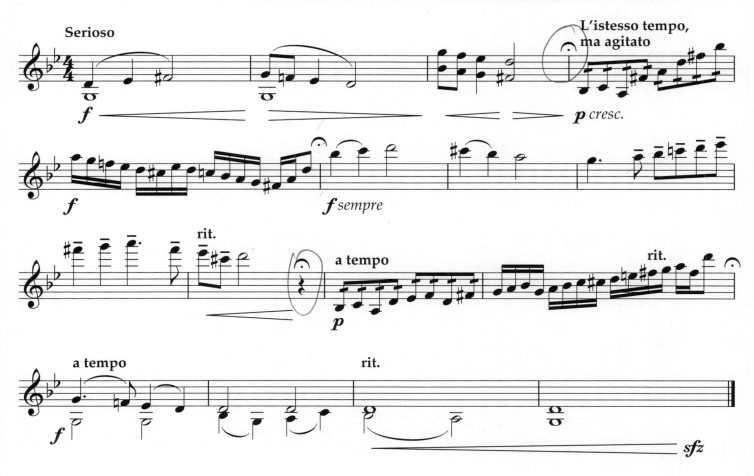

26

Grade 8 Stage 3

Rhythmic exercises

Compound time signatures may be felt against a ♪ or ♩. pulse, or a mixture of the two. As you become more experienced at reading these time signatures you will become adept at working out which pulse is the most appropriate.

Melodic exercises

Set 1: Exploring

Set 2: More cross rhythms and compound time signatures

Prepared piece

1 Play all the scales and arpeggios used in this piece.

2 Scan through the piece and decide if there are any tricky rhythms. Think them through.

3 Scan again, looking for finger patterns, repeated patterns and any passages which may catch you out.

4 Read the piece through in your head, in time, hearing it as best you can.

5 Study the last bar for about 15 seconds, then play it from memory.

6 Now play the piece as if you've been learning it for months! Don't lean forward or peer at the music as you play – relax and enjoy it!

Ski-ing through the Swiss countryside

Going solo! Don't forget to prepare each piece carefully before you play it.

March for Martians

Here is the six o'clock news ...

Grade 8 **Stage 4**

Rondo: The magic violin ... with a hint of Mozart

Carnival time ... with a hint of Dvořák

Pepper from *The seasonings* … with a hint of Vivaldi

Transylvanian toccata … with a hint of Bartók

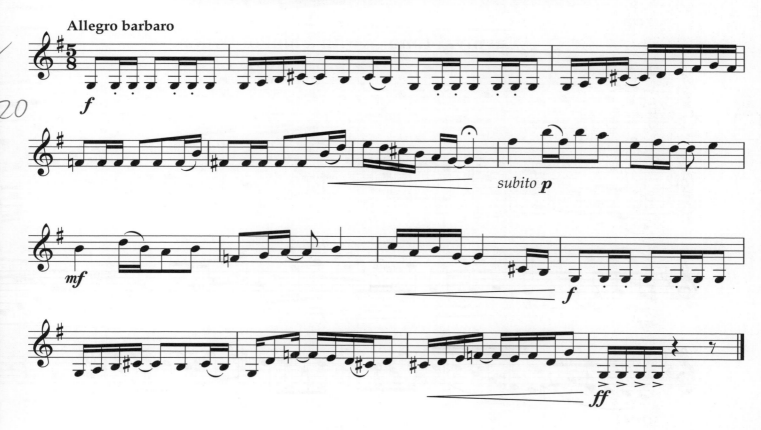

Ballad ... with a hint of Malcolm Arnold

Mustard and cress ... with a hint of Gershwin